This Book Belongs To:

Jada Wimbush

Smile,
you are Magnificent!

For Monty, Nelly, and Omari you are my inspiration:

I love you three to the moon and beyond!!!

This book is dedicated to children of

color from all around the world

You are **beautiful**

You are **amazing**

You are **Magnificent**

First U.S. Paperback Edition 2020

ISBN - 978-1-7348518-0-9

Published by Holland Jordan
For information on bulk purchases please contact:
Holland Jordan
P.O. Box 366503
Atlanta, GA. 30336

info@mochamonty.com

Magnificent MOCHA MONTY

by Holland Jordan

Illustrated by:
Mosaku Ogooluwa & Illustrationpal/Sam

I love my mocha skin

so **Magnificent** and brown

Monty
M

I love my mocha mouth it

makes such a **Magnificent** sound

M

I love my mocha ears so

Magnificent and not too small

SCHOOL BUS
M

I love my **Magnificent** mommy

who's very, very tall

I love my **Magnificent** mocha hands

they're just the right size for me

M

One day when I grow older

I'll use them to climb a **Magnificent** tree

M

I love my mocha legs

and my **Magnificent** mocha feet

I rock them back and forth when

I'm dancing to a beat

M

I'll repeat

I love my **Magnificent** mocha skin

I love my **Magnificent** mocha mouth

I love my **Magnificent** mocha ears

I love my **Magnificent** mommy

I love my **Magnificent** mocha hands

I love my **Magnificent** mocha legs

I love my **Magnificent** mocha feet

But most of all I love

my **Magnificent** mocha eyes

now turn this page very, very slowly

for a really nice surprise

I love my mocha eyes

this is really true, and right now

my mocha eyes are looking at

Magnificent, Amazing

You!!

Children are great imitators so give
them something great to imitate

Children are the world's most valuable
resources so treat them like they are

Diamonds might be precious but,
children are priceless

Reading gives children a place to go without
ever having to leave where they are

Each one, reach one, teach one

It's our responsibility

ABOUT THE AUTHOR

Holland Jordan is a licensed master social worker (LMSW) who was honorably discharged from the U.S. Army at the rank of Staff Sergeant. She has been employed as an HIV case manager, school social worker, and preschool teacher. Holland recently retired from her position as a medical social worker for one of the largest healthcare systems in the United States to pursue her love of writing.

Holland graduated from the University of California, Berkeley, and holds degrees in early childhood development, behavioral science, sociology and a masters in social work. She is a mother, grandmother and mentor to many in her community. This is her first book, inspired by her oldest grandson, Monty. Holland divides her time between California and Georgia where her grandchildren live.

ILLUSTRATORS

Illustrationpal/Sam is an experienced, dedicated and professional illustrator who excels in vector portraits, caricatures, color pencil and digital illustrations. He is very passionate about his work and loves to tell stories through his illustrations. **Mosaku Ogooluwa**, a Renaissance visual artist from Nigeria, is the CEO of Goldinhma Creativity. In addition to illustration, he has a wide knowledge in 2D/3D arts and design, VFX, motion graphics, animation, sound design, crafts making and other art forms.

MONTY'S STORY

One hot summer day, after playing in the backyard, my 3-year-old grandson Monty and I decided to sit down and take a rest. We sat for a few minutes in our lawn chairs not talking but just breathing and enjoying our time together. Out of the blue he looked at me with his big brown eyes and said, "Grandma Abuela, I want to look just like you." Somewhat taken aback by his comment, I asked "You want to wear clothes like Grandma?" He became very quiet, appeared sad, and looked down at his shoes. Without ever looking up at me he said, "No Grandma Abuela, I want my skin to look like yours." (I have a honey/beige skin tone and Monty has the most beautiful mocha brown skin tone.) In that very moment I felt as if my heart had been ripped out of my body and I could feel a tear forming in my eye. I thought to myself: Who has told my 3-year-old grandson something is wrong with the color of his skin and why? I realized immediately that Monty felt ashamed of his skin.

I knelt down in front of him, looked him straight in the eye and replied, "Monty you are magnificent, you are amazing, you are blessed." The smile that began to form on his face was a sight to see. He pointed his finger at himself and said, "Grandma Abuela, I'm magnificent, I'm amazing." I replied, "You are Magnificent Mocha Monty with the most Magnificent Mocha skin." He began running around the yard shouting to his mom who was in the house. "Grandma Abuela says I am magnificent and amazing; I am Magnificent Mocha Monty!"

A NOTE FROM THE AUTHOR

When children are taught to "Love the skin they're in" and encouraged to celebrate who they are, children will believe they can achieve anything. Telling kids how awesome and incredible they are must be a 365-day-a-year ritual. Magnificent Mocha Monty builds self-esteem and promotes self-confidence in children of color; however, this book is not solely written for one demographic. It is important for all children to see and read about kids who are different than they are and to see them in a positive light. When we open up our children's hearts and minds at a very early age to diversity and inclusion, they grow up to become adults who treat others with dignity and respect.

It is my goal to promote acceptance of diversity to children of all colors one book at a time!

Holland Jordan

When you buy the book *Magnificent Mocha Monty*, Monty will contribute a portion of each purchase to the Tuskany Falls animal sanctuary. Monty loves animals and believes every animal deserves a good life. To learn more about Tuskany Falls visit www.tuskanyfalls.com and read about Starbuck the gentle pig and many other animals. Do a good deed and give to animals in need.

Special Section for Educators

Hello Educators! Attached you will find a detailed interactive read aloud lesson and several activities that will build your students comprehension skills in relation to *Magnificent Mocha Monty.*

WHY AN INTERACTIVE READ ALOUD?

Interactive Read Aloud Lessons provide several benefits to students. Read aloud lessons promote listening skills, vocabulary development, comprehension skills, and most importantly, a chance for your students to hear a fluent reader in the moment.

ACTIVITY INSTRUCTIONS

Each activity has been created to assist pre-readers, beginning readers, and advanced readers in your classroom. These activities are engaging and connect to literacy standards to make them even more meaningful. After reading the text, make copies of the activities and give them to your students. Make sure to read the directions for the students and answer any clarifying questions. Just that simple!

National Governors Association Center for Best Practices, Council of Chief State School Officers. (2010). Common core state standards. Washington D.C.: Author. http://corestandards.org

Magnificent Mocha Monty

Author: Holland Jordan **Genre:** Fiction **Focus Skill:** Determine Theme

Standards

RL.K.1: Ask and answer questions about key details in a text.
RL.K.2: Identify the main topic and retell key details of a text.
RL.K.7: Describe the relationship between illustrations and the text
SL.K.2: Understand text read aloud orally and answer questions about key details

Vocabulary (Tier 2)

Magnificent: very beautiful (1)
Mocha: brown (3)
Surprise: unexpected present (16)
Amazing: great (17)

Book Introduction

Today, we're reading *Magnificent Mocha Monty* by Holland Jordan. This story is about a little boy named Monty (point to his picture on the cover) embracing what is unique about himself. Let's read and find out what makes Monty so magnificent!

Questions

(1) Q: How is Monty feeling in this picture? How do you know? (Have students mimic the facial expression.)
A: Monty is feeling happy in this picture. I know because he's smiling in the illustration.

(5) Q: What are some things Monty might hear with his ears?
A: Let students share their responses (ex: music, laughter, etc.)

(7) Q: Monty and his mother look different; what are some of their differences?
A: Let students share their responses (ex: Monty is short, and his mother is tall. Monty has short hair, and his mother has long hair, etc.)

(16) Q: I wonder what our surprise will be! (Have students share if time permits.) Lets keep reading to find out…

(18) Q: How are you similar to or different from Monty?
A: Let students share their responses.

(End) Q: What does the author want us to learn from the story?
A: The author wants to teach us that we are magnificent. (Introduce new vocabulary: confidence, self-esteem, and self-love.)

Magnificent Mocha Monty

Author: Holland Jordan **Genre:** Fiction **Focus Skill:** Determine Theme

Standards

RL.1.1: Ask and answer questions about key details in a text.
RL.1.2: Identify the main topic and retell key details of a text.
SL.1.2: Understand text read aloud orally and answer questions about key details.
SL.1.6: Use complete sentences to complete task.

Vocabulary (Tier 2)

Magnificent: very beautiful (1)
Mocha: brown (3)
Surprise: unexpected present (16)
Amazing: great (17)

Book Introduction

Today, we're reading *Magnificent Mocha Monty* by Holland Jordan. This story is about a little boy named Monty (point to his picture on the cover) embracing what is unique about himself. Let's read and find out what makes Monty so magnificent.

Questions

(1) Q: How is Monty feeling in this picture? How do you know? (Have students mimic the facial expression)
A: Monty is feeling happy in this picture. I know because he's smiling in the illustration.

(5) Q: What are some things Monty might hear with his ears?
A: Let students share their responses (ex: music, laughter, etc.)

(7) Q: Monty and his mother look different; what are some of their difference?
A: Let students share their responses. (ex: Monty is short, and his mother is tall. Monty has short hair, and his mother has long hair, etc.)

(16) Q: I wonder what our surprise will be! (Have students share if time permits.) Lets keep reading to find out…

(18) Q: How are you similar or different from Monty?
A: Let students share their responses.

(End) Q: What does the author want us to learn from the story?
A: The author wants to teach us that we are magnificent. (Introduce new vocabulary: confidence, self-esteem, and self-love.)

Sequencing with Monty

Name: ______________________________

Directions: Oh no! The story is out of order. Sequence the story correctly by writing the numbers 1-6 in the circles provided.

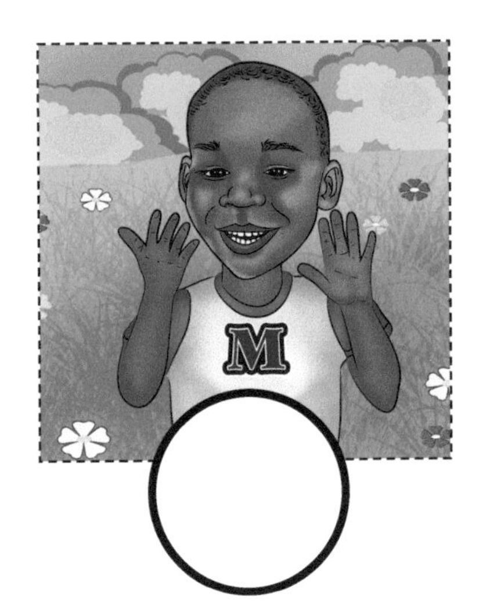

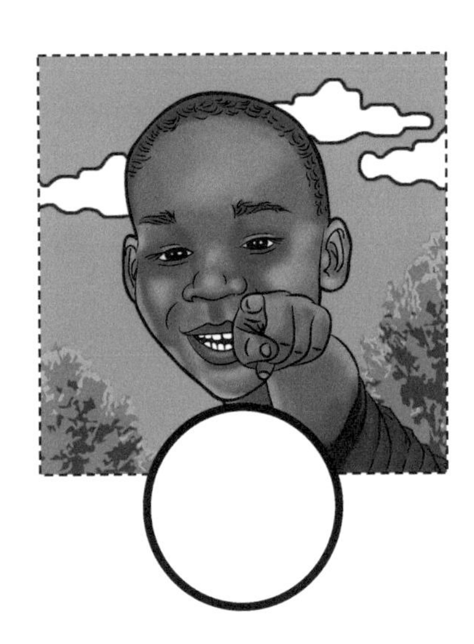

Magnificent ME

Directions: Draw a picture of yourself and then write what you love about being MAGNIFICENT!

Name: ____________________

I love my Magnificent

____

I love my Magnificent

____

I love my Magnificent

____

I love my Magnificent

____

Monty & Me

Name: ______________________________

Directions: Draw a picture of Monty and a picture of yourself. Write how you and Monty are the same, and how you both are different.

MONTY

How are you and Monty the same?

____

____

____

____

How are you and Monty different?

____

____

____

____

ME

If you enjoyed reading ***Magnificent Mocha Monty*** look for:

Mocha Monty and His Cousins Nate and Noah
(Coming Soon!)

Visit www.mochamonty.com

Please leave a review on Amazon - we appreciate them!
Subscribe to our website for updates.
Follow and like us on Instagram.